CONTENTS

SUPERMAN
RETURNS ™
ANNUAL 2007

Pedigree®

Published by Pedigree Books Limited
Beech Hill House, Walnut Gardens, Exeter, Devon EX4 4DH.
E-mail books@pedigreegroup.co.uk
Published 2006

Based on the Superman Returns Movie Storybook by Benjamin Harper.
Superman created by Jerry Siegel and Joe Shuster

£7.99

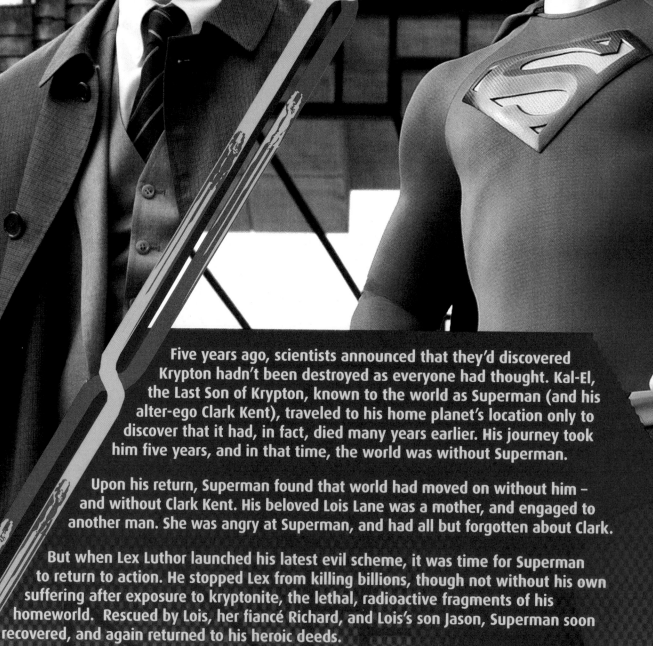

Five years ago, scientists announced that they'd discovered Krypton hadn't been destroyed as everyone had thought. Kal-El, the Last Son of Krypton, known to the world as Superman (and his alter-ego Clark Kent), traveled to his home planet's location only to discover that it had, in fact, died many years earlier. His journey took him five years, and in that time, the world was without Superman.

Upon his return, Superman found that world had moved on without him – and without Clark Kent. His beloved Lois Lane was a mother, and engaged to another man. She was angry at Superman, and had all but forgotten about Clark.

But when Lex Luthor launched his latest evil scheme, it was time for Superman to return to action. He stopped Lex from killing billions, though not without his own suffering after exposure to kryptonite, the lethal, radioactive fragments of his homeworld. Rescued by Lois, her fiancé Richard, and Lois's son Jason, Superman soon recovered, and again returned to his heroic deeds.

Daily Planet

When Superman left Earth to look for Krypton five years ago, Lois Lane was left alone; lost in a world of uncertainties. Heartbroken that the man she loved left without saying goodbye, she picked up the pieces and forged ahead. She met Richard White, a *Daily Planet* editor, and eventually had a son named Jason.

Still hurting five years later, Lois wrote an editorial for the *Planet* titled "Why the World Doesn't Need Superman," which won her a Pulitzer Prize. But when the Man of Steel returned, she questioned her own thoughts. Perhaps, she realized, the world *does* need a Superman.

While investigating a citywide blackout, Lois stumbled upon Lex Luthor's fiendish plot. With the help of her son and fiancé, Lois escaped from Lex's clutches. But she soon returned to save Superman from the kryptonite-laden crystals of Lex's new continent, "New Krypton."

With Superman's return and many questions still troubling her, there are many adventures ahead for the intrepid reporter.

Lois Lane may have written the article "Why the World Doesn't Need Superman," but it was Lex Luthor who benefited the most from the Man of Steel's five-year disappearance. He'd been imprisoned for two consecutive life sentences, but was released early after Superman didn't appear to testify against him in court.

Released from prison, Lex took care of the elderly and ailing Gertrude Vanderworth, inheriting her vast fortune when she died. He used that money to travel to the arctic, finding Superman's Fortress of Solitude, and stealing the powerful crystals from it to create a new continent on Earth, wich he called New Krypton.

Nearly killing Superman with the kryptonite laden continent, Lex appeared to be successful in his plot. But when Lois rescued Superman, it allowed him to throw New Krypton into space, ending Luthor's hoped-for conquest. Lex's plot was further derailed when his girlfriend, Kitty Kowalski, dumped the remaining crystals out of their escape helicopter.

Kitty and Lex escaped from Superman, and found themselves marooned on a small desert island. Lex may be down for now, but he is certainly not out. He has sworn revenge on Superman, and promises to return. Next time, he swears, he will be victorious.

He fell in love with Lois Lane. He takes care of her son. He can fly (planes, that is). And he is the nephew of *Daily Planet* editor in chief Perry White. In the time that Superman was gone, Richard White grew to prominence not only as the best international editor for the world's greatest metropolitan newspaper, but also in Lois Lane's life.

He would do anything for his fiancée, and her son Jason. He proved this time and time again, but no more so than flying his seaplane into the heart of a tumultuous storm to save Lois and Jason. And then, only because Lois asked him to, he returned to the stormy sea to save Superman.

Richard doesn't know about Jason's apparent superstrength. But it doesn't matter. He loves the boy, and he loves Lois, and they are his highest priority.

For years Perry White has led the *Daily Planet* newspaper to the top of the game in the industry. He is always gruff, holding the highest of expectations for his news staff. Only his nephew Richard and intrepid reporter Lois Lane have been able to get away with arguing with their boss.

When Superman returned from his five-year mission in space, Perry mobilized his team, covering the story from every different angle. Even Lois's pleas to write about the strange blackout were overruled, since she and Superman had a history together. When Clark Kent came back to the newspaper looking for a job, Perry rehired him – but only because another reporter had recently passed away!

Perry survived the earthquake damage to the *Daily Planet*, and thanked Superman for saving the historic globe that sat atop the Planet building. He's got a keen intellect, and a nose for news. Just *don't* call him chief!

DAILY PLANET™

He was always Superman's pal, and Clark Kent's best friend. Jimmy Olsen, the youngest member of the *Daily Planet* staff, has spent the five years without Superman working his way up the ladder to become a highly demanded photographer for the paper. His friendship with Clark was very important to him, and he talked often of their adventures together.

When Clark came back from his five year absence, Jimmy excitedly filled him in on all the happenings, including Lois's status as a fiancée and mother. When he realized that the news upset Clark, he took his old friend out for a drink, where Clark made the decision to become Superman again.

Jimmy's loyalty to his friends is matched only by his talent as a photographer. He captured the now-famous shot of Superman carrying the Daily Planet globe on his shoulder. Even more impressively, he recognized Lois's handwriting on a partial fax she sent, detailing her location when Lex had her and Jason hostage. He helped save her, and still managed to get a good picture or two. All in a day's work for Superman's pal.

SUPERPOWERS

Superman has amazing abilities far beyond those of mortal men! He gets his powers by exposure to the Earth's yellow sun. But what specifically are these superpowers?

Read below to learn what makes Superman so special!

FLIGHT

Look! Up in the sky! It's a bird! It's a plane!

It's Superman! Soaring high above the citizens of Metropolis, Superman uses his ability to fly to help send the experimental space shuttle into space, save Lois Lane's plummeting airplane, and even take an entire continent up into outer space! Lois has reminded him that Richard is a pilot and therefore can also fly, to which the Man of Steel replies: "Not like this!"

SUPERSPEED

Faster than a speeding bullet! While growing up in Smallville, Clark Kent loved to run as fast as he could. Cutting a trail through the corn that his family grew on the farm, Clark was almost invisible, he was traveling so quickly! As Superman, he continues to use his speed, running and flying faster than the eye can see.

X-RAY VISION

The ability to see through solid objects has always been of use to Superman. By staring at walls, doors, and even in Lois Lane's purse, Superman focuses his eyes and "peels" away the top layer to see what is inside. The only thing he can't see through is lead. In any case, this is a very helpful power to have when you're trying to save people – you can see where they are!

SUPERBREATH

Superman's lungs are strong. Very strong. So strong, in fact, that he has superbreath! With the ability to take large amounts of air in his lungs, and compress it like in a scuba tank, Superman can release a mighty burst of breath, strong as wind, and ice cold. He has used it in situations from freezing things to blowing out Lois Lane's cigarette lighter.

SUPERSTRENGTH

The longer Superman is exposed to the rays of Earth's yellow sun, the more energy his body absorbs. This energy gives him tremendous strength—he is a living solar battery. His muscles are tight, and like an ant, allow him to lift much more than his own body mass. Superman must always be careful to keep his strength in check, or else he could seriously injure someone. Even when fighting bad guys, he holds back to avoid causing irreparable damage.

INVULNERABILITY

Doctors can't get needles in his skin. Bullets are stopped when they hit his body. Even explosions do little damage. Superman is invulnerable. Even his costume seems resistant to usually-harmful substances bad guys try to use. Some people might claim to be bulletproof, but Superman's invulnerability makes him so!

SUPERHEARING

Richard White asked Lois Lane if Superman could hear everything separately or all at once. She replied, simply, "Both." Indeed, Superman's phenomenal superhearing lets him hear the individual cry for help, as well as the large, mass cries of people around the world. The Man of Steel hears it all, and it is his personal call to action.

HEAT VISION

Like a million tiny solar powers, Superman collects massive amounts of solar radiation, giving him his superpowers. But this solar radiation also puts off tremendous heat. Lois once commented that she'd forgotten how warm he was. There seems to be only one way to release this heat – through the eyes, of course! Superman's heat vision cuts through solid objects, melts metal, and is so intense it can even burn underwater, allowing him to cut New Krypton free.

Daily Planet
Crossword Puzzle

Welcome to the *Daily Planet* Crossword Puzzle.
Use the clues below to fill in the spaces in the puzzle.

ACROSS
3. Ace reporter
4. Clark Kent's hometown
8. The Man of Steel
9. Superman's home planet
10. Superman's Kryptonian father
11. Lois and Clark's boss
12. Lois's son's name
13. Lex's yacht
14. Superman's weakness

DOWN
1. Superman's secret identity
2. Superman's arch-enemy
5. Clark's best friend
6. Where Clark and Lois work
7. Lex's girlfriend

14

SUPERMAN RETURNS™

The Story

The crystal ship zoomed through space, its sole occupant dormant in a sleep pod. Soaring past stars toward its destination, the ship awakened its sleeping passenger with an alarm. A star chart appeared, showing Superman that he was nearing the end of his journey – what he hoped would be the planet Krypton. Could astronomers' reports that his home planet was still intact and showing signs of life be true?

Touching a crystal on the control panel, Superman turned off the alarm. With the touch of another crystal, he opened a transparent panel so he could see what was outside. All Superman could see was a darkness so vast that it blocked out the stars.

Turning on a massive beam from his spacecraft, Superman illuminated what was in front of him – a huge, black planet. His hopes rising that Krypton actually had survived the blast that allegedly destroyed it so many decades before, Superman brought his spacecraft in for a closer look.

Crystal cities, monuments, and canyons came into view, but there was something wrong. They looked dark and quiet, not bright and glowing, as cities should be.

Something else was wrong too. Superman was beginning to tremble and he felt slightly sick. A single bead of sweat dripped from his brow as he tried to fight off the sensations and move on.

Superman maneuvered his craft through the broken ruins of a massive dome and descended into a deep canyon. Large monoliths were arranged in a circle around the perimeter of the canyon. As Superman inspected the monoliths, he noticed that a hieroglyph was carved into each one.

He stopped suddenly when he came across a hieroglyphic symbol that looked familiar – the symbol on his costume, the symbol of his Kryptonian heritage.

As he was gazing at the monolith, a crippling pain shot through his body. Leaning forward and bracing himself, he peered out the winder of his craft to see a faint green glow radiating from the monolith.

Kryptonite!

Trying to get away before the kryptonite could do too much damage, Superman zoomed his ship away from the monolith toward what he thought was the edge of a cliff. When he arrived, however, he was amazed to discover that the cliff actually dropped off into nothingness – he had been exploring only a chunk of what once had been the planet Krypton!

Superman realized that he was trapped in the middle of an asteroid field made up of nothing but kryptonite. Huge chunks of the green rock whizzed by his ship, and as each passed, Superman could feel more and more of the strength draining from his body. Superman was trying desperately to get out of the asteroid field before his strength completely left him when a truck-size chunk of kryptonite slammed into the side of his shop, smashing a section of the hull and throwing Superman to the floor. The damaged portions of the ship grew back, repairing themselves almost immediately.

Superman struggled to get to his feet as the kryptonite asteroids continued their assault. A kryptonite asteroid the size of a golf ball smashed into a window, shattering it.
As the crystals of the window worked to re-form themselves, Superman punched a series of commands into the ship's console and then managed to whisper one word –
"Home." Taking one last look at the remnants of the home he never knew, Superman crawled back into his sleeping pod as an image of Earth appeared on the ship's console.

Martha Kent heard a low, deep rumbling. She looked out her kitchen window to see bright red clouds of dust rising as a meteorite slammed into the earth.

Martha rushed to her pickup truck and followed the trench the meteorite had made until she came to its resting place. There she saw the charred remains of Superman's crystalline ship, still glowing from re-entry.

She jumped as someone touched her from behind.

"Mom..." Superman gasped as he collapsed into her arms.

"In spite of your past, I know you're a good man," Gertrude Vanderworth said to the man sitting at her bedside in the luxurious Vanderworth mansion. The frail old woman was holding his hand. "And all good men deserve a second chance."

As she spoke, surrounded by the medical equipment that kept her alive, her family was outside, banging on the door to get in. The man pushed her last will and testament into her hands so she could sign it.

"You said that if I helped you get out of prison that you'd take care of me. And you have. You've done so much for me. And that's why you deserve everything."

As she signed her will, she said, "I love you, Lex Luthor." With that, she was gone.

Lex Luthor, criminal mastermind and Superman's sworn arch-enemy, exited Gertrude's room and stunned her relatives by handing over the will stating that the entire Vanderworth shipping fortune was now his to do with as he pleased.

"You can have this," he joked, ripping the wig from his shiny, bald head and tossing it to a little girl. "The rest is mine."

He then motioned to the maid, who was busy dusting, to join him. He and the maid, who actually was Lex's girlfriend, Kitty Kowalski, then left the shocked family and exited the mansion.

21

Back on the Kent family farm, Clark Kent was just waking up. He was in his old bedroom, the one he had slept in since his parents had first found him in that meteorite crater so many years ago – before he had discovered that he actually was Superman, a being sent from another planet to protect Earth.

Clark looked up at the ceiling and saw the small stars that had been glued there since he was a child. It was so good to be home!

"Hey, boy," Clark said to the family dog as he rolled over in his bed. Clark was still in pain from his journey, but he managed to get dressed and head downstairs.

Descending the staircase, Clark looked at the photos from his childhood. They brought back memories – birthday parties, working on the farm with his father, his high school graduation – nothing to suggest that he was actually Superman.

Clark walked outside to take a look at the farm where he had spent so many years. It had fallen into disrepair since his father died. The machinery sat rusted and unused, and the fields of corn were overgrown and untended. Clark took a deep breath of the morning air and then knelt down to run his fingers through the soil. As he did, a flood of childhood memories came rushing back.

When Clark was much younger, he had been doing his chores when he fell through the barn roof. The wood roof splintered beneath Clark's feet as he crashed through, but he didn't hit the ground – he hovered just above it! He could *fly*!

Terrified by what he had just experienced, Clark ran out of the barn and into the cornfield. He realized he was running faster than anything he had ever seen before. Everything around him was a blur.

Suddenly he yelled and leapt up into the air! He sailed over the cornstalks and landed, still running. He tried again - and he jumped even higher! Every time he landed, he ran and jumped again, and every time he went higher. He ran with all his might, closed his eyes, and bounded into the air once more. He soared even higher than before.

After he landed, Clark opened his eyes and realized he was on top of the old grain silo. He was half a mile away from the farm and had traveled all that way in a matter of seconds!

"Wow!" Clark whispered. He was stunned.
How on earth had he done what he did?

Gathering all his courage, Clark pushed off the grain bin up into the air. He rocketed straight through the air and over the entire cornfield. Using his house as a springboard, he jumped up again, soaring toward the barn. But he was going too fast – he was going to...crash!

He slammed through the barn roof and braced for a hard landing...but nothing happened. Opening his eyes, Clark realized he was hovering above the ground again. He was baffled, so he stood up and fell over on purpose this time. Still he hovered! Then he noticed something else amazing – his glasses had fallen off, yet he could see perfectly. What was going on?

Clark looked over and noticed a strange handle sticking out from the barn floor. Lowering himself to the ground, he pulled the handle, opening a door in the floor. Peering through the door, Clark saw a set of stairs leading down to a cellar he had never seen before!

He walked down the steps cautiously, not knowing what to expect. There was a large object covered with a tarp. Brimming with curiosity, Clark pulled the tarp away to reveal a crystal structure that looked like a meteor. It was hollow, as if something had been inside. He approached it to get a closer look.

When he peered inside, he discovered a gleaming crystal. It was humming, as if it was calling to him. Clark reached in and picked it up. When he touched it, a white glow flooded the room. He examined it carefully – it was beautiful, like nothing he had ever seen. At that moment Clark knew the crystal was meant for him and that somehow this discovery would explain the amazing things he had experienced that morning. He knew he had to talk to his parents and learn the truth.

Waking from his memories, Clark walked into the barn. He noticed stacks of *Daily Planet* newspapers throughout the barn and started sifting through them until he came across one that made him stop. "Why the World Doesn't Need Superman – by Lois Lane," the headline read. "For five long years the world has stared into the sky, waiting, hoping and praying for his return," the article stated. "We have spent our days asking where he went, debating why he left, and wondering if he's even alive...."

Clark folded the newspaper sadly and walked back into the house.

Clark was considering staying at the farm for a while and fixing it up. Lois Lane's article made him feel as if he were no longer needed, and he was tired of leading a secret life, hiding who he really was from his friends.

He had told them all he was going off to explore the world. His mother had sent Lois postcards to make her think that Clark was traveling the globe instead of searching for his home planet. Martha Kent knew that Clark couldn't turn away from his destiny – that wasn't why he was sent to Earth. "Your father used to say that you were put here for a reason. And we all know it wasn't to work on a farm," Martha said to Clark.

He knew she was right.

DRAW A COSTUME 1

In *Superman Returns*, the Man of Steel wears two different uniforms: his silver space suit, and his traditional costume. In the space opposite draw a unique costume for Superman to wear as he prepares for an undersea adventure. (Remember, he can hold his breath for a long time, but not forever!)

ULTIMATE SUPERMAN

Think you know the Man of Steel, as he appeared in Superman Returns?

Take our twelve-page Ultimate Superman Returns Quiz and find out if you're the Man of Steel of Superman Returns Trivia!

Questions are: true/false, multiple choice, fill in the blank, matching, and come from the storybook, the film itself, and some challenging behind-the-scenes info.

Answers are at the bottom of page

TRUE OR FALSE?   T   F

1. True or False: Superman discovered that Krypton was still intact.

2. True or False: Lois's fiancé, Richard White, is *Daily Planet* editor-in-chief Perry White's son.

3. True or False: Superman's Kryptonian father is named Jor-El.

4. True or False: Superman testified against Lex at his parole hearing.

5. True or False: Kryptonite helps Superman grow stronger.

6. True or False: Lois's son can play the piano.

MULTIPLE CHOICE

7. What is Lois Lane's son's name?

a) Jason
b) Jerry
c) Jimmy

8. How long was Lex Luthor supposed to be in prison?

a) One life sentence.
b) Two life sentences.
c) 20 years.

9. What was the name of Superman's home planet?

a) Kelvin
b) Krypton
c) Epsilon

10. What is Clark Kent's dog's name?

a) Shelley
b) Shelton
c) Shelby

11. What newspaper do Lois Lane and Clark Kent work for?

a) The *Daily Star*
b) The *Daily Planet*
c) The *Metropolis Poste*

12. The actress who plays billionairess Gertrude Vanderworth is known for playing what Superman character on television?

a) Lois Lane in *The Adventures of Superman*
b) Martha Kent in *Lois & Clark: The New Adventures of Superman*
c) Lois Lane's mother in *Smallville*

WHO AM I?

Superman Returns features some of the most beloved characters of all time. How well do you know them? Read the clues and write the *Superman Returns* character's name in the space provided. Answers are at the bottom of the page.

1. I am an editor at the *Daily Planet*.
My uncle is also an editor at the *Planet*.
I can fly a seaplane.
I am engaged to Lois Lane.

2. I interviewed Superman.
I won the Pulitzer Prize.
I have a son named Jason.
I am engaged to Richard White.

3. I was released from prison early.
I have a yacht called *The Gertrude*.
I have creepy friends.
I'm bald.

4. I was gone for five years.
 I am a reporter for the *Daily Planet*.
 I grew up in Smallville, Kansas.
 I wear glasses

5. I can play the piano.
 I get bad marks in gym, but good ones in science.
 I'm related to Lois Lane.

6. I was gone for five years.
 I am very fast.
 I can fly.
 I wear a cape.

8. I made Clark a welcome back cake.
 I recognized Lois's handwriting on her fax.
 I am a photographer for the *Daily Planet*.
 I like bowties.

DRAW A COSTUME 2

In *Superman Returns*, the Man of Steel wears two different cotumes: his silver space suit, and his traditional uniform. In the space opposite draw a suit for Superman to wear as he prepares for an adventure into the molten core at the center of the Earth!

Near the North Pole, a yacht called *The Gertrude* was making its way through a nasty storm. Inside, Lex Luthor was surrounded by articles about Superman and the planet Krypton, and was busy reading books on crystals and minerals.

Trying to explain to Kitty what they were doing at the North Pole, Lex said, "Whoever controls technology controls the world."

"We've found something!" one of his men interrupted. He showed Lex the information he had discovered.

"That's it! Drop anchor!" Lex shouted.

Lex and his crew trekked through the icy landscape, Kitty complaining the entire time. One of his men grabbed onto some ice for support, but the ice was warm! "You were right – there's some sort of unnatural weather pattern keeping it hidden," Stanford, one of Lex Luthor's henchmen, said, looking at his equipment.

"I'm always right," Lex responded.

They had found what they were looking for. They were in front of a huge structure made entirely of the same crystal structures found on Krypton. They had discovered Superman's Fortress of Solitude!

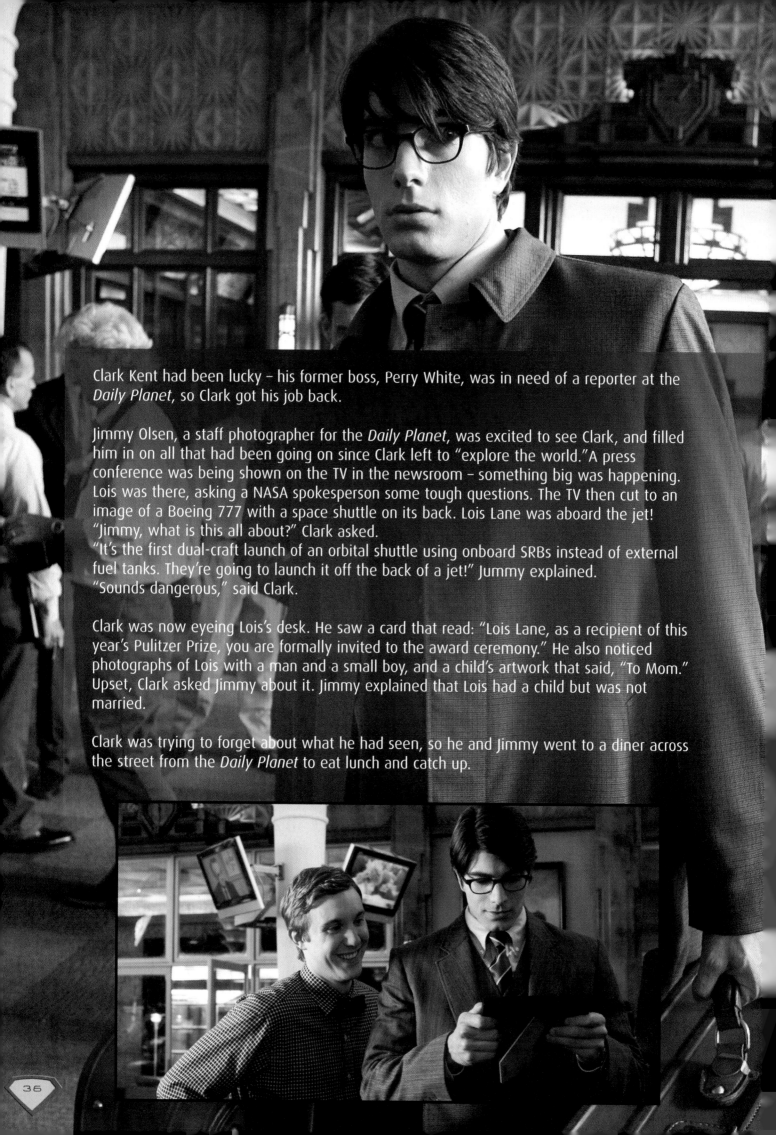

Clark Kent had been lucky – his former boss, Perry White, was in need of a reporter at the *Daily Planet*, so Clark got his job back.

Jimmy Olsen, a staff photographer for the *Daily Planet*, was excited to see Clark, and filled him in on all that had been going on since Clark left to "explore the world." A press conference was being shown on the TV in the newsroom – something big was happening. Lois was there, asking a NASA spokesperson some tough questions. The TV then cut to an image of a Boeing 777 with a space shuttle on its back. Lois Lane was aboard the jet!
"Jimmy, what is this all about?" Clark asked.
"It's the first dual-craft launch of an orbital shuttle using onboard SRBs instead of external fuel tanks. They're going to launch it off the back of a jet!" Jummy explained.
"Sounds dangerous," said Clark.

Clark was now eyeing Lois's desk. He saw a card that read: "Lois Lane, as a recipient of this year's Pulitzer Prize, you are formally invited to the award ceremony." He also noticed photographs of Lois with a man and a small boy, and a child's artwork that said, "To Mom." Upset, Clark asked Jimmy about it. Jimmy explained that Lois had a child but was not married.

Clark was trying to forget about what he had seen, so he and Jimmy went to a diner across the street from the *Daily Planet* to eat lunch and catch up.

"This place is so tacky. Lex, why are we back here?" Kitty asked in disgust as she and Lex walked through the Vanderworth mansion.

"Kitty, while you were doing your nails, I was unlocking the secrets of one of the most advanced civilizations in the universe," Lex Luthor responded. "You see, unlike our clunky earth-bound methods of construction, the technology of Krypton was based on manipulating the growth of crystals." As the group headed down into the basement, Lex continued: "Cities, vehicles, weapons. Entire continents! All grown, not built. To think, one could create a new world with such a simple little object." With that, he removed the white crystal he had discovered in the Fortress of Solitude. "It's like a seed. All we need is water." "Like sea monkeys!" Kitty exclaimed. "Yes," Lex agreed. "Like sea monkeys." With a flip of a light switch, Lex revealed a sprawling and incredibly detailed model train set, complete with miniature people and cities. Above the set planes and jets circled, suspended by wires. Peering through a microscope, Stanford used a tiny saw to carve a sliver from the Kryptonian crystal. As he carried it to Lex, he tripped over a wire and sent the sliver flying right into a lake on the model. With a hiss, all power in the mansion went out.

RACE TO

Daily Planet NEWSROOM

Lex Luthor has stolen several crystals from Superman's Fortress of Solitude.

He will use them to create a new continent on Earth, threatening billions of people!

Who can stop him?!

Cut out the *Superman Returns* characters on the right hand side. Each player chooses one to challenge Lex. Using a die, take turns rolling, and moving from the

Start

Perry White is yelling for you. Return to the Newsroom

A source tells you Lex is on his yacht. Take another turn.

Large amounts of kryptonite slow you down. Lose a turn.

Bank robbers get in your way. Move back one space.

You fly fast. Move ahead four spaces.

STOP LEX ◇◌ǐǐ⊖-💻♾

Daily Planet bullpen all the way to Lex's new continent.

Some of the squares you stop on will help you out in your quest to save the world, but beware because there are some obstacles in your way, too! The first person to reach Lex flips a coin to determine if he beats Lex! Heads you win, tails the evil Lex Luthor does.

You know a shortcut. Move ahead one space.

You've won the Pulitzer Prize. Move ahead three spaces.

Kitty Kowalski needs saving. Move back three spaces.

Captured by Lex Luthor! Return to the Newsroom and start over.

Finish

ULTIMATE SUPERMAN

FILL IN THE BLANK

13. _____ Kent is Superman's adoptive mother.
a) Mary
b) Martha
c) Melissa

14. _____ -El is Superman's Kryptonian name.
a) Kal
b) Zor
c) Jor

15. Lex's yacht is named The _____.
a) *Gosper*
b) *Gratitude*
c) *Gertrude*

16. Jimmy's favorite pub, where he takes Clark, is the _____.
a) Club Metropolis
b) Bo's
c) Ace o' Clubs

17. _____ is the new space shuttle Superman rescues upon his return.
a) *Expedition*
b) *Explorer*
c) *Excalibur*

18. Clark Kent grew up in _____.
a) Metropolis
b) Smallville
c) Krypton

MATCHING

DRAW A LINE FROM THE CLUE TO THE ANSWER

19. Superman

A. Saw llamas

20. Clark Kent

B. Superman's pal

21. Lex Luthor

C. Lost control of her car

22. Kitty Kowalski

D. Returned after five years away

23. Jimmy Olsen

E. Won the Pulitzer Prize

24. Lois Lane

F. Obtained the Vanderworth fortune

LOST LEX

Lex Luthor has discovered the Fortress of Solitude, but a storm is preventing him from reaching it.

Help guide his yacht to the Fortress of Solitude.

START

FINISH

YOUR SECRET IDENTITY

When Superman goes to work at the *Daily Planet*, he is disguised as mild mannered reporter Clark Kent. His disguise is very simple, but very effective: he combs his hair differently, and wears a pair of eyeglasses. With your parent's help, cut out the pair of glasses below, and then cut out their eyeholes and the small black holes, so that you can tie them to your head. With these on, no one will know your secret identity!

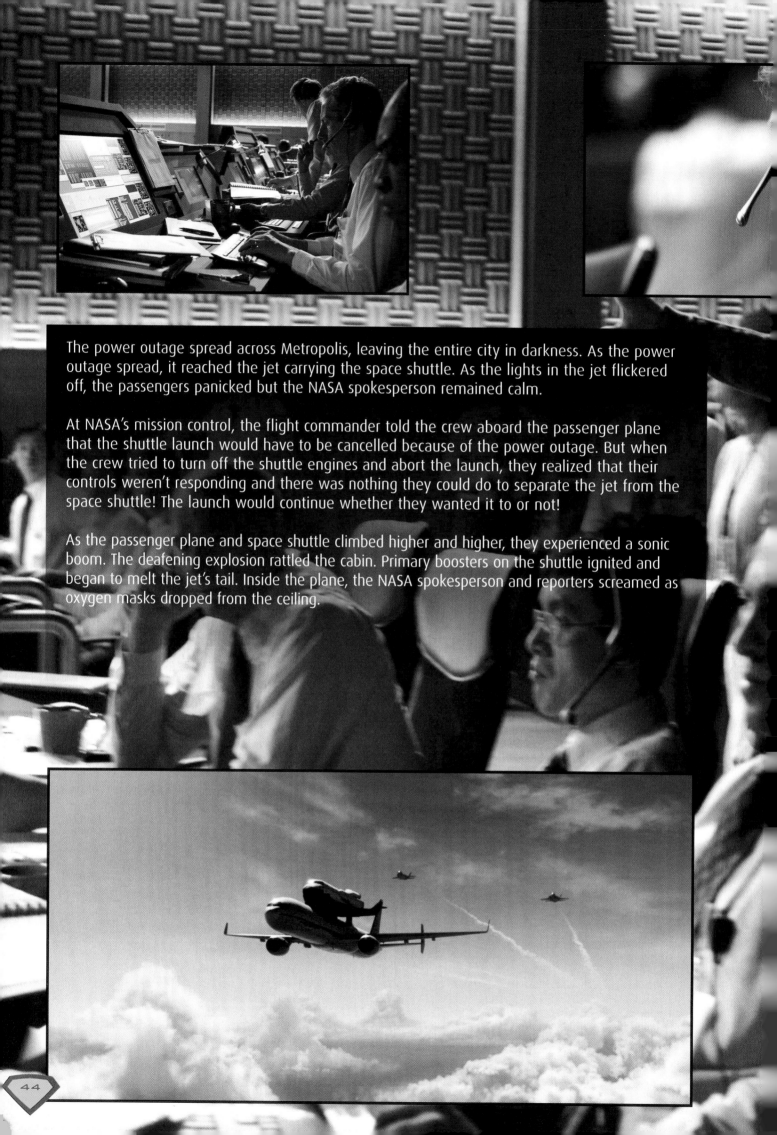

The power outage spread across Metropolis, leaving the entire city in darkness. As the power outage spread, it reached the jet carrying the space shuttle. As the lights in the jet flickered off, the passengers panicked but the NASA spokesperson remained calm.

At NASA's mission control, the flight commander told the crew aboard the passenger plane that the shuttle launch would have to be cancelled because of the power outage. But when the crew tried to turn off the shuttle engines and abort the launch, they realized that their controls weren't responding and there was nothing they could do to separate the jet from the space shuttle! The launch would continue whether they wanted it to or not!

As the passenger plane and space shuttle climbed higher and higher, they experienced a sonic boom. The deafening explosion rattled the cabin. Primary boosters on the shuttle ignited and began to melt the jet's tail. Inside the plane, the NASA spokesperson and reporters screamed as oxygen masks dropped from the ceiling.

Back at the diner, Clark saw what was happening on one of the diner's TVs and sprang into action. He leapt from his seat and raced to change into Superman. As he ran into an alley and pulled his shirt open, he realized he had left his costume in a suitcase back at the Daily Planet! He raced back into the office and changed into his costume, slipping past reporters and editors who were too busy watching what was happening on TV to notice him flying out of a window.

The shuttle and jet approached the mesosphere as Superman sped toward the out-of-control crafts. Just as he approached them, the shuttle's booster rockets fired, blowing the jet's tail completely off and sending Superman spiralling backward!

Superman struggled to regain control so he could catch up to the jet and pry it loose from the shuttle. Breaking the sound barrier, Superman soared back toward the jet and shuttle.

Inside the jet, Lois strapped herself in. Looking out the window, she saw the blue sky fading to black and then Superman speeding past. Unsure of herself, she did a double take – did she really see that?

Outside, Superman landed on the roof of the jet, placing himself between it and the shuttle. Superman used all his strength to pry the two apart. Couplings holding the crafts together snapped under his power, and the vehicles separated. With all his might, Superman pushed the shuttle up and away from the jet, allowing it to soar safely into space.

"We have lift-off. I mean, we're in orbit. Everything's okay!" the shuttle commander reported to mission control.

The passengers aboard the jet felt a momentary sense of calm once they detached from the shuttle, and then realized their worries were far from over as the plane started to plummet back toward Earth!

Spiralling out of control, the jet sped toward the ground as Superman raced to catch it. He tried to grab onto the right wing to slow the descending craft, but it was no use – the wing just snapped off. Pieces of the jet flew everywhere as it raced closer and closer to the ground.

Finally, Superman braced himself against the nose of the jet, pushing with all his might in an attempt to slow the plane's fall.

As the batter hit a fly ball, the spectators at a baseball stadium watched it soar upward when their eyes caught sight of Superman pushing against the nose of the spiralling jet. All the players on the field rushed out of the way as Superman and the jet sped toward the baseball diamond.

Inside the jet, Lois closed her eyes. Everyone around her screamed hysterically. They were doomed.

Superman looked behind him and saw the baseball diamond. With one last shove, he pushed with all his strength, and the jet's descent ended. Metallic groans filled the air as Superman stopped the falling plane a few feet above the ground. Gently, Superman lowered the damaged jet onto the grass.

Inside, the stunned passengers didn't know what to think. What had happened? As the rescue slide inflated, Superman stepped inside. "Is everyone all right?" he asked. "I suggest you all stay in your seats until medical attention arrives."

Out from behind a seat came a shocked Lois Lane. She hadn't seen Superman in years, and here he was right in front of her!

"Are you okay?" Superman asked as she stood up nervously. Lois opened her mouth to say something, but couldn't get anything out.

Superman made sure she was okay, and then said "I hope this incident hasn't put any of you off flying. Statistically speaking, it's still the safest way to travel."

And with that, he stepped off the jet.

The crowd at the baseball stadium sat in stunned silence while Superman's image flashed on the huge monitors above the seats. As the spectators began to realize what they had just witnessed, their silence transformed into thunderous applause – Superman was back!

WORD JUMBLE

Lex Luthor has an evil plan to create a new continent! Unscramble the Superman-related words below, and then place the letter in each yellow square in the spaces at the bottom of the page to discover the name of Lex's new home.

MSPRNAUE

SLIO ELNA

REPRY HWIET

LRCAK TEKN

TFSORESR FO DUTOLSEI

MJIMY ENSOL

DLIYA TLENAP

HRAMTA NKET

EXL HROUTL

PYKNTTIROE

ANSWER:

_ _ _   _ _ _ _ _ _ _ _

Answers: SUPERMAN, LOIS LANE, PERRY WHITE, CLARK KENT, FORTRESS OF SOLITUDE, JIMMY OLSEN, DAILY PLANET, MARTHA KENT, LEX LUTHOR, KRYPTONITE. Combine the letters Answer: NEW KRYPTON

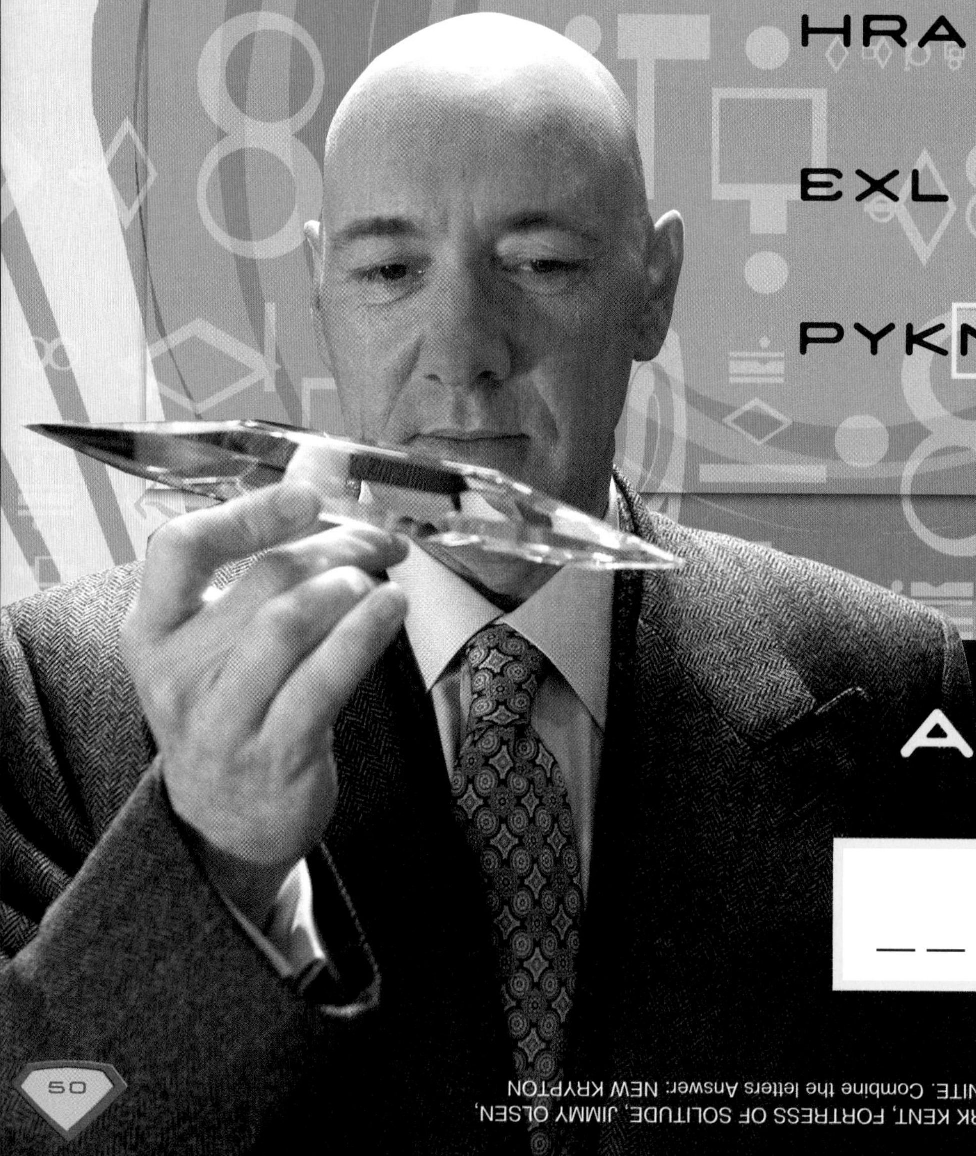

ULTIMATE SUPERMAN

MULTIPLE CHOICE

25. Where is the Fortress of Solitude located?

a) The Amazon

b) The Arctic

c) Antarctica

26. What famous comic book cover was recreated when Superman rescued Kitty?

a) *Action Comics #1*

b) *Superman #1*

c) *Man of Steel #1*

27. What article won Lois Lane her Pulitzer Prize?

a) "Why the World Doesn't Need Superman"

b) "Why the World Needs Superman"

c) "Superman Lives!"

28. Which of the following was NOT one of Lex's henchmen?

a) Stanford

b) Brutus

c) Ian

29. Actor Jack Larson (Bo the Bartender) has NOT also appeared in which Superman television series?

a) *The Adventures of Superman* (as Jimmy Olsen)

b) *Smallville* (as Jimmy Olsen's father)

c) *Lois & Clark: The New Adventures of Superman* (as an aging Jimmy Olsen)

30. Which DC Comics super hero is on Jason's pajamas at the end of the film?

a) Batman

b) Green Lantern

c) Aquaman

TRUE OR FALSE?　　T　F

31. True or False: *Superman Returns* is dedicated to Christopher and Dana Reeve.

32. True or False: *Superman Returns* screenwriters Dan Harris and Michael Dougherty appear in the film as college students at the Metropolis Museum of Natural History.

33. True or False: This is director Bryan Singer's first comic book-based movie.

34. True or False: Actor Kevin Spacey shaved his head to play Lex Luthor.

35. True or False: According to the design on the main floor, the Daily Planet building was built in 1938.

36. True or False: The footage of Marlon Brando portraying Jor-El was originally shot for 1978's *Superman: The Movie*.

DESIGN A DOORHANGER

FORTRESS OF SOLITUDE

DO NOT DISTURB

When Superman needs to get away from it all for a bit, he goes to the Fortress of Solitude, just like you go to your bedroom! In the space provided on the door hanger left, draw a picture of what your Fortress of Solitude would look like.

Then, with an adult's help, cut out the door hanger, and let everyone know that you want some solitude!

WORD SEARCH

Throughout his historic comic book career, Superman has faced many, many villains besides Lex Luthor. See if you can find the names of his many enemies in the word search below. They can be found going up, down, forwards, backwards and diagonally.

AMAZO
BIZARRO
BLACKROCK
BRAINIAC
CONDUIT
DARKSEID

DOOMSDAY
GOG
KRYPTONITE MAN
LEX LUTHOR
LIVEWIRE
MONGUL

MR. MXYZPTLK
PARASITE
PRANKSTER
RUIN
TOYMAN
ZOD

G	K	R	Y	P	T	O	N	I	T	E	M	A	N	V
A	O	F	E	R	I	W	E	V	I	L	X	W	B	I
J	P	A	R	A	S	I	T	E	F	J	E	G	I	C
F	R	X	O	R	M	H	G	B	P	A	V	S	Z	N
C	A	C	I	E	I	O	A	K	Z	O	D	D	A	E
O	N	H	F	W	G	I	N	L	Y	C	E	M	R	D
N	K	Y	D	A	L	L	X	G	K	B	Y	V	R	L
D	S	B	A	K	E	I	O	Q	U	O	T	P	O	C
U	T	M	R	M	X	Y	Z	P	T	L	K	A	M	A
I	E	L	K	C	L	T	N	A	X	M	S	Y	N	I
T	R	P	S	N	U	J	I	O	M	U	Y	O	C	N
X	J	V	E	L	T	C	L	V	O	A	H	L	A	I
N	W	A	I	E	H	A	R	U	I	N	Z	I	K	A
M	G	L	D	O	O	M	S	D	A	Y	R	O	X	R
L	Z	D	I	I	R	K	C	O	R	K	C	A	L	B

55

KRYPTONIAN

On Superman's home planet Krypton, they used an alphabet very different from our own. Look at the table below to learn the translation of Kryptonian symbols and English letters.

Then on the next page, practice your new language skills by decoding the Kryptonian words. (Hint: they are names of Superman characters.)

Then, at the bottom of the page, try writing your name using the Kryptonian symbols.

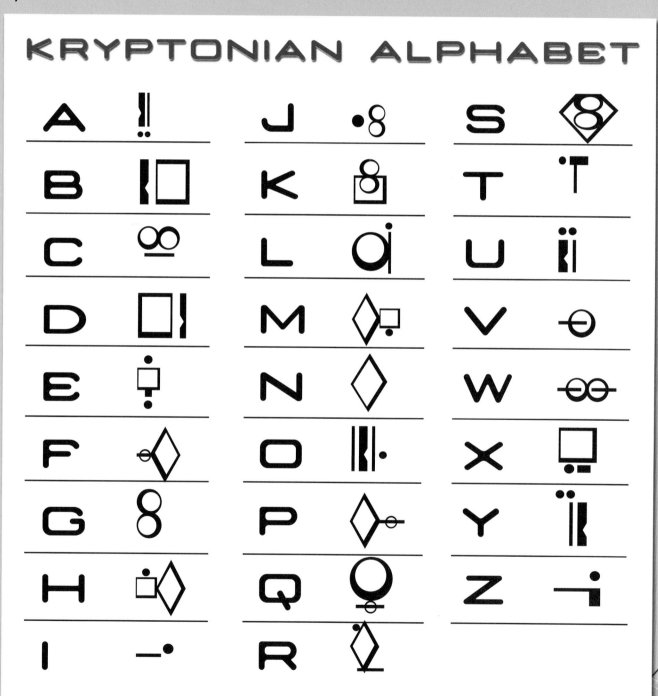

KRYPTONIAN ALPHABET

CODE

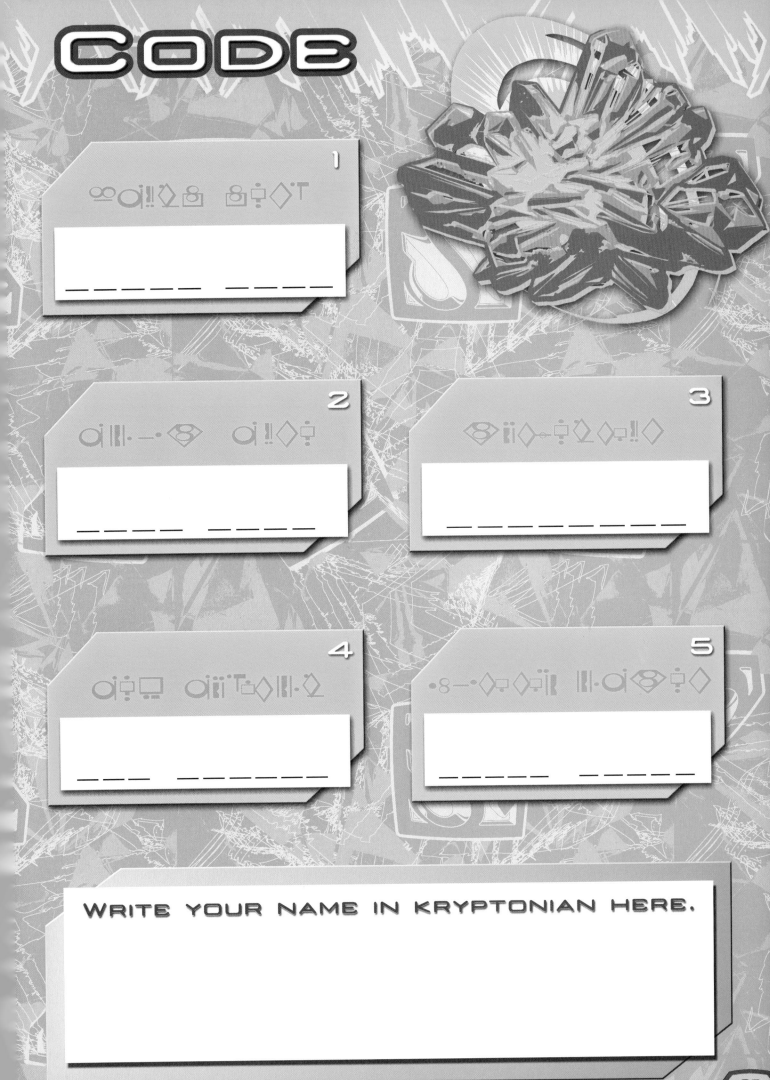

1

_ _ _ _ _ _ _ _ _ _

2

_ _ _ _ _ _ _ _ _ _

3

_ _ _ _ _ _ _ _

4

_ _ _ _ _ _ _ _ _ _

5

_ _ _ _ _ _ _ _ _ _

WRITE YOUR NAME IN KRYPTONIAN HERE.

Meanwhile, back at the Vanderworth mansion, there was chaos. The model train set was a smoky ruin. Where miniature cities had been, huge crystalline structures had sprouted that were identical to those in the Fortress of Solitude. The crystal shards shot straight up through the ceiling and spread roots down through the floor.

"Lex, your little crystal broke everything," Kitty said.
"Yes, so it did." Lex whispered.

Superman was big news the next day, and Perry White wanted all the angles covered. He assigned Lois the task of getting an exclusive interview with Superman, but she protested. She had more important things to investigate – specifically, the unexplained blackout that had caused so much trouble throughout the city.

"The story isn't about the blackout! It's about Superman!" Perry lectured.
As Lois left Perry's office, she told him she would get the Superman story, but she really was off to work on another story – the blackout.

Then she saw Clark.
"Clark! Welcome back!" she said.
Clark tried to make small talk but was nervous – he hadn't seen her in a long time. Not only did Lois have a son, she also had a boyfriend – Richard White, nephew of Perry White, and an editor for the *Daily Planet*.

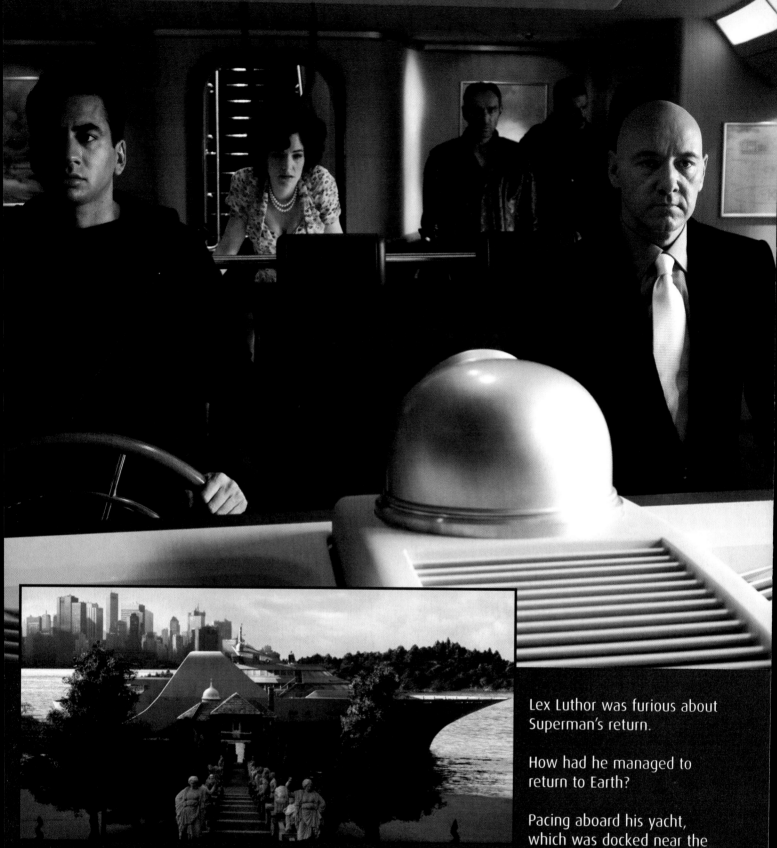

Lex Luthor was furious about Superman's return.

How had he managed to return to Earth?

Pacing aboard his yacht, which was docked near the Vanderworth mansion, Lex was joined by his henchmen. They had just returned from stealing a rocket and its launcher and were carrying it in a large crate.

"So, what are we going to do?" Stanford asked. "You're going to modify it according to the plans and attach it to the stern of the ship." "No, I mean about him!" Stanford said, referring to Superman. He and Lex had worked long and hard to make it seem as if there was life on Krypton, and he was angry that Superman had managed to return to Earth in one piece.

Then Lex saw it – a newspaper headline that gave him the answer. "World's Largest Collection Of Meteorites On Display At Metropolis Museum Of Natural History"

"Hey, Clark. How's your first week back at work?" Lois asked at the *Daily Planet* the next morning.

"It's okay. Kind of like riding a bike," Clark responded.

As the two kept talking, the conversation came back to Superman. Lois had been hurt that Superman had left without saying goodbye to her.

"Well, maybe saying goodbye was so hard because he didn't know if it would be goodbye for a little while, or goodbye forever," Clark said sympathetically.

"What's so difficult about it?" Lois said, upset.

Trying to change the subject, Clark asked if she would like to have lunch. Lois couldn't, but she invited him out to her home in the suburbs for dinner instead.

Superman was flying through the city when he happened upon Lois' home. He heard her inside talking to Richard about Superman's return. He heard Lois tell Richard that she was no longer in love with Superman. Saddened, Superman flew high into the sky.

As Superman flew higher, he heard an alarm go off – he swooped back down and caught four robbers on the roof of a bank. They were throwing bags of money into a helicopter and were getting ready to take off. The bank was surrounded by police officers on the ground. There was no way the robbers were going to give up – they pulled a large machine gun out of a crate and were getting ready to open fire on the police when two bank security guards sneaked up behind them and started shooting. As the robbers turned to fire back, Superman landed between them and deflected the bullets!

"What took you so long?" the bank security guards asked when the SWAT team finally burst onto the roof.

The SWAT team couldn't believe what they saw – each of the robbers had been tied up with a bent helicopter blade and were swaying in the breeze.

Across town, a car completely out of control crashed through the streets. The woman behind the steering wheel screamed hysterically, spinning the wheel to avoid hitting people. As the car careened through the panicked streets, it bounded into a park, racing around benches and trees as people scattered to get out of the way.

Surely the car was going to crash, but suddenly the driver realized she was hovering above the park! As her car descended gently to the ground, she saw that Superman had come to her rescue.
"Miss, are you all right?" Superman asked the driver.

"My heart!" the driver screamed. As she collapsed, Superman caught her in his arms.
It was Kitty Kowalski.
"Heart palpitations! I have heart palpitations and a murmur!"

Superman tried to tell her that he couldn't see anything wrong with her but she begged him to take her to the hospital.

SPECIAL SIGHT

ARE YOUR EYES AS SUPERPOWERED AS SUPERMAN'S?

LOOK CLOSELY AT THE TWO PICTURES BELOW AND FIND THE DIFFERENCES BETWEEN THEM! ANSWERS ARE BELOW.

Answers: 1) There is no "S" emblem on his belt. 2) The "S" emblem on superman's chest has changed colour. 3) Superman's curl of hair on his forehead is missing. 4) Part of his cape on his right shoulder is missing. 5) The bottom right of his cape is missing

SEARCH FOR A SYMBOL

ONLY TWO OF THESE SUPERMAN SYMBOLS ARE IDENTICAL. WHICH TWO?

ARE YOU A LEX OR SUPERMAN?

TAKE THIS QUIZ
AND FIND OUT!
CHOOSE ANSWERS
A, B OR C AND
THEN READ YOUR
SCORE BELOW.

1. You see a wallet fall out of a man's pocket. Do you:
a. take it?
b. return it to the man?
c. return the wallet but keep the money inside?

2. You're eating lunch when you see a car about to crash into a building. Do you:
a. continue eating your lunch?
b. rush out and prevent the crash?
c. call the police and let them deal with the results of the accident?

3. It looks like a little lost kitten is about to get eaten by a big dog. Do you:
a. reward the dog with a biscuit?
b. stop the dog and save the kitten?
c. hope that the dog is only fooling?

4. You see that Kitty Kowalski is about to slip on a banana peel and fall flat on her face. Do you:
a. laugh as she slips on it and falls?
b. pick up the banana peel and thus prevent her from stepping on it?
c. do nothing?

HOW TO FIGURE YOUR SCORE:

Give yourself 1 point for every "A" answer that you've chosen, 10 points for every "B" answer, and 5 points for every "C" answer.

You're a Lex Luthor if your score is between 4 and 20, and a perfect Superman if your score is 40! Anything in between is room for worry, mate!

Daily Planet

No.8930 ■ THURSDAY JULY 13 2006 ■ METROPOLIS NEWSPAPER OF THE YEAR   60p

WHATS ON AT THE MUSEUM?

REPORT BY CLARK KENT PAGE 3

METROPOLIS MUSEUM

Lex Luthor spotted

Lex Luthor was spotted by a number of people outside the Metropolis Museum only yesterday, a police report revealed. The official statement is that until there is some hard evidence of Mr. Luthor's return to Metropolis, no action will be taken

NEWS Pages 6, 7

Gertrude Vanderworth has died.

The elderly widow of Stephen Vanderworth has recently passed away. Stephen Vanderworth inherited his vast wealth from his grandparents, and then used his own skill to expand the Vanderworth Company into a worldwide conglomerate. Gertrude's death has bought more than just sadness to them. On her deathbed, she signed away her fortune to a mysterious stranger. The family is left penniless and grief-stricken.

NEWS Pages 6, 7

My Interview With _____

Picture of _____

INTERVIEW BY LOIS LANE

LOIS Lane has been known to get the big interviews in her career! She broke the story on Superman's return, and got the exclusive interview. But this interview is her biggest yet. It's with you!
Write out, answers to the questions, telling the world about yourself. Then draw or past a picture of yourself in the space provided on the above.

What's your name?
_____

When is your birthday?
_____

How old are you?
_____

Tell me a little about your family:
_____
_____
_____
_____
_____
_____

67

Lois Lane's World Famous Interview Continues...

What's your favorite ice cream?

_____

What's your favorite color?

_____

Tell my about the biggest adventure you've ever had:

_____
_____
_____
_____
_____
_____
_____
_____
_____
_____
_____

If you could have one of Superman's powers, which would you pick? Why?

_____
_____
_____
_____
_____
_____
_____
_____
_____
_____
_____
_____
_____
_____
_____
_____
_____
_____
_____
_____
_____

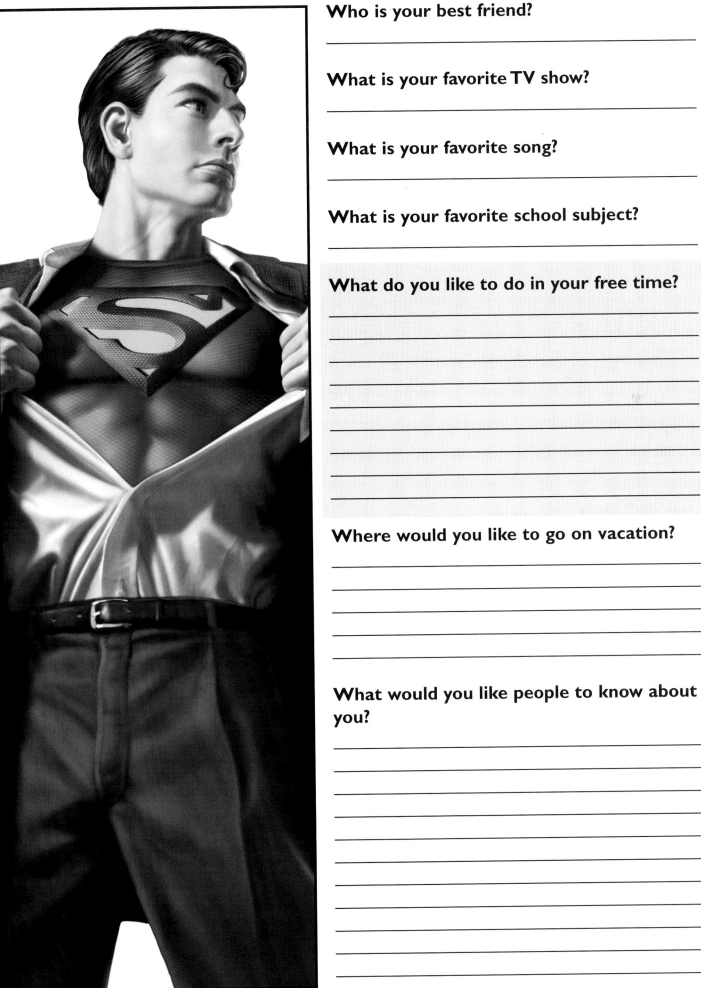

Who is your best friend?

_____

What is your favorite TV show?

_____

What is your favorite song?

_____

What is your favorite school subject?

_____

What do you like to do in your free time?

_____
_____
_____
_____
_____
_____
_____
_____

Where would you like to go on vacation?

_____
_____
_____
_____

What would you like people to know about you?

_____
_____
_____
_____
_____
_____
_____
_____
_____
_____

Supermans secret identity- Clark Kent

ODD SUPERMAN OUT!

WHICH ONE OF THESE SUPERMAN IS NOT LIKE THE OTHER TWO?

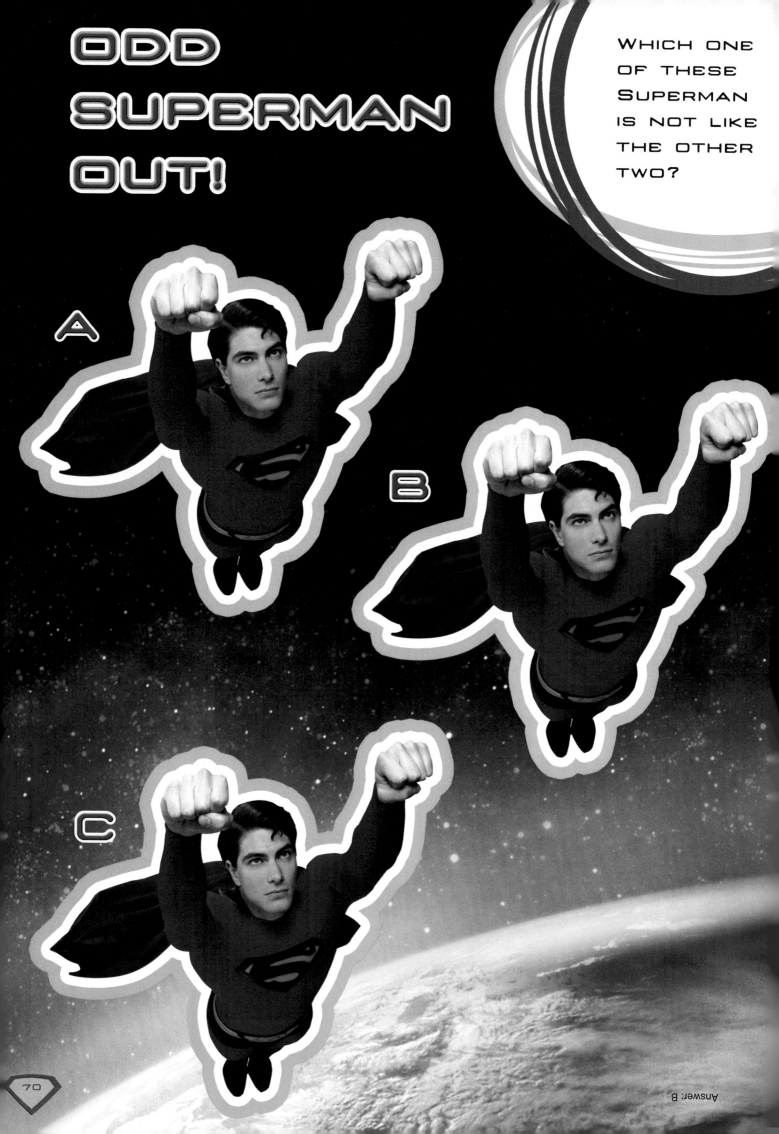

A

B

C

Answer: B

WHICH SUPERPOWER? PART 1

Cross out all the letters which appear more than once. Then rearrange the remaining letters to spell one of Superman's superpowers.

B	A	B	H	E	T
J	N	A	M	U	S
G	O	R	I	R	U
F	D	S	C	J	C
D	N	L	M	O	E

ANSWER: _ _ _ _ _ _

WHICH SUPERPOWER?
PART 2

Go through the maze of desks at the *Daily Planet* newsroom and write down only the leters that you pass in order to get out. To find the right way out the letters must inscramble to spell the name of one of Superman's superpowers!

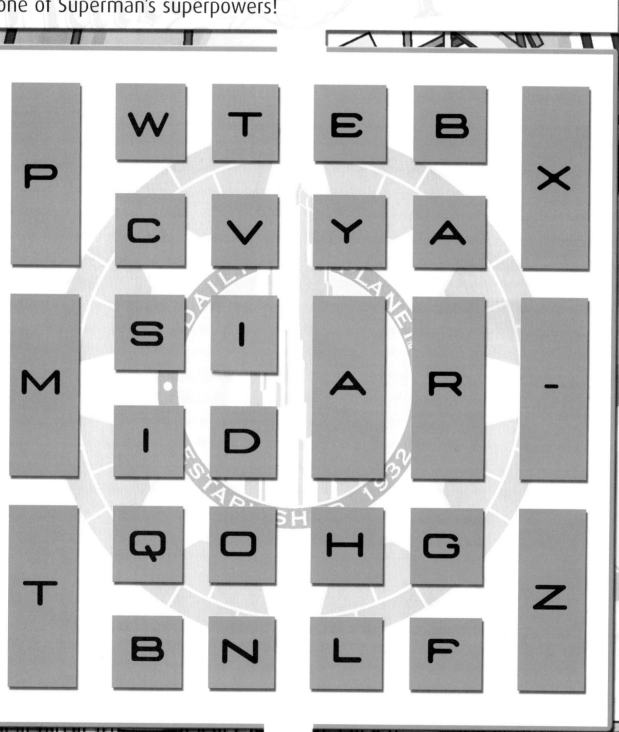

ANSWER: ___ ___ ___ ___ ___   ___ ___ ___ ___ ___ ___

SUPERMAN'S SHADOW

Which shadow from A-E matches Superman's blue shadow?

WORD SEARCH

See if you can find the Superman terms in the box below. They read forward, backward, up, down, and diagonally.

SUPERMAN
JASON
CLARK KENT
RICHARD WHITE
LOIS LANE
GERTRUDE

LEX LUTHOR
VANDERWORTH
KITTY KOWALSKI
FORTRESS
JIMMY OLSEN
SEAPLANE

PERRY WHITE
DAILY PLANET
KRYPTON
CRYSTAL
MA KENT
BRUTUS

J	A	R	E	T	I	H	W	Y	R	R	E	P	H	I
I	V	O	D	A	I	L	Y	P	L	A	N	E	T	A
M	N	H	Q	S	A	Z	G	E	R	T	R	U	D	E
M	R	T	Y	L	U	H	X	C	S	L	L	Y	C	H
Y	I	U	W	I	J	P	L	K	E	A	O	M	S	T
O	C	L	A	R	K	K	E	N	T	L	I	I	T	R
L	H	X	V	S	M	G	A	R	A	N	S	C	I	O
S	A	E	K	E	A	L	D	T	M	J	L	M	U	W
E	R	L	B	Y	P	O	S	E	N	A	A	H	R	R
N	D	C	R	A	F	Y	M	O	I	K	N	S	H	E
X	W	B	E	K	R	D	T	R	E	D	E	E	O	D
N	H	S	L	C	N	P	V	N	O	E	Z	L	C	N
H	I	D	N	X	Y	J	T	B	R	U	T	U	S	A
W	T	F	O	R	T	R	E	S	S	R	A	L	E	V
P	E	I	K	S	L	A	W	O	K	Y	T	T	I	K

DRAW A COSTUME 3

In *Superman Returns*, the Man of Steel wears two different costumes: his silver space suit, and his traditional uniform. In the space below draw a suit for Superman to wear as he prepares for an adventure to the frozen ice planet of Frigidox, where the average temperature is 500 degrees below freezing!

FIND THE WORDS

THERE ARE AT LEAST 60 SMALLER WORDS THAT YOU CAN MAKE
FROM THE WORD "SUPERMAN" (EXCLUDING PLURAL WORDS).
HOW MANY CAN YOU MAKE?

Here are some examples to help you get started.

SUM   MANE   RUSE   NAP

ULTIMATE SUPERMAN

WRITE THE WORD THAT CORRECTLY COMPLETES THE SENTENCE.

Lex Luthor

Kryptonite

Heat vision

Jason

Coordinates

Camera phone

FILL IN THE BLANK

37. Lois and _____ were held captive on the *Gertrude*.

38. A young man used his _____ when Superman saved Kitty.

39. With his _____, Superman removed New Krypton from the ocean floor.

40. Gertrude left her fortune to _____

41. _____ is lethal fragments of Superman's home world.

42. Lois faxed her _____ to the *Daily Planet,* leading to her rescue.

MATCHING

DRAW A LINE FROM THE CLUE TO THE ANSWER

43. Stanford   A. *Superman Returns* **director**

44. Perry White   B. **Co-creator of Superman**

45. Bobbie-Faye   C. **Lex's henchman**

46. Ben Hubbard   D. **Martha's best friend**

47. Jerry Siege   E. *Daily Planet* **editor-in-chief**

48. Bryan Singer   F. **NASA representative**

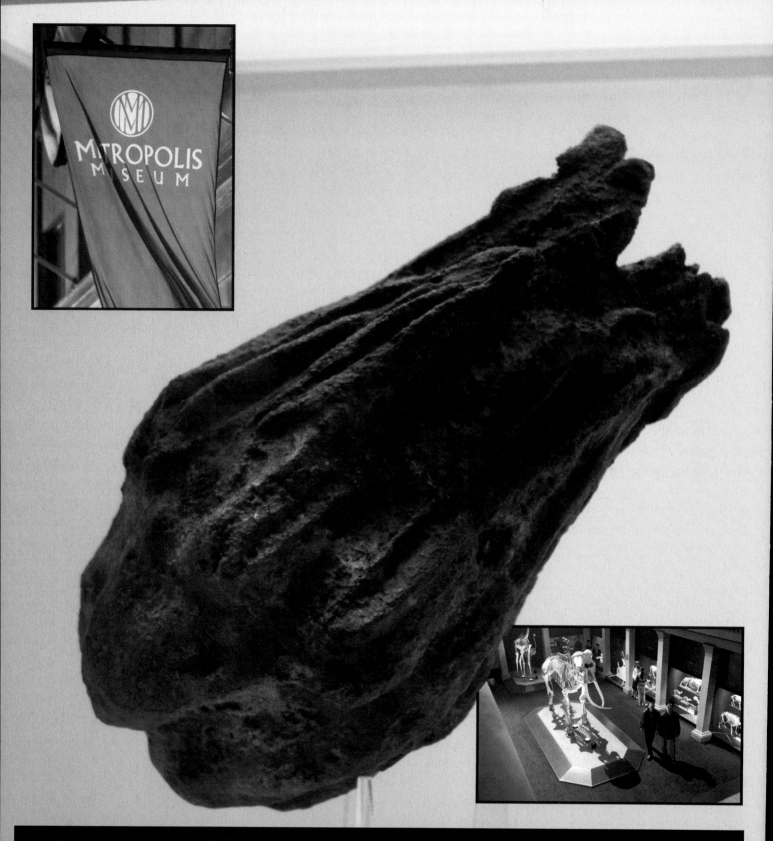

At the same time, Lex and his men were getting off a tour bus. They were dressed as tourists, complete with souvenir T-shirts and disposable cameras. They were in front of the Metropolis Museum of Natural History. "I'm sorry, we close in 10 minutes," the security guard warned. "We only need five," Lex said as he and his men rushed into the museum. At the meteorite exhibit, they all took pictures with their cameras until they came across a meteorite from Addis Ababa. This was the one!

Lex broke the case and grabbed the meteorite, and alarms sounded throughout the museum. As the guards rushed in, Lex's henchmen turned to take their pictures – zap!
The cameras were actually stun guns, and the guards slumped to the floor. Triumphantly, Lex chipped at the meteorite's exterior. As the faint green glow became more prominent, Lex knew he had what he wanted – kryptonite!

Back on his yacht, Lex stood in front of a map of the world, placing a pin at the intersection of several lines, when Kitty walked in.

"I was going to pretend the brakes were out, like we talked about. PRETEND! You didn't have cut them!" Kitty screamed. "What are those lines?" she asked, changing the subject, as usual.

"Those lines? They are 12 fault lines. As for the pin," he said. "The pin is where we're going." Up on the bridge, Stanford had the rocket on the counter, with all of its inner parts removed. He looked at the hollow compartment on the rocket and then measured the meteor they had stolen. Most of its outer shell had been chipped away, revealing a thick inner layer of kryptonite. As Stanford continued to cut into the meteor, Lex noticed a shard of kryptonite that had fallen onto the counter. He picked it up and slipped it into his pocket.

At the Daily Planet, Perry White had made some changes. Clark and Lois now were working together on the blackout story, and Richard was going to help Lois on the Superman story.

Lois and Clark were beginning to work when Lois said she needed a break. She left Clark to go up to the roof for some fresh air. While she was on her way, Clark changed into his Superman costume and surprised Lois as she stepped out the door.

As the two began to talk, Lois asked him about where he had gone and what he had hoped to find. Soon the conversation turned more personal – Superman brought up the article that had won Lois the Pulitzer Prize.

"Why did you write it?" Superman asked.

After Lois explained, he apologized for hurting her.

"You didn't hurt me. You didn't hurt any of us. You just helped us find the strength to take care of ourselves. That's why I wrote the article – the world doesn't need a savior."

Superman took Lois into his arms and they flew high into the evening sky.
He wanted to show her something. They had flown so high that everything was silent. "What do you hear?" Superman asked Lois.

"Nothing. It's quiet." Lois replied.

"Do you know what I hear? *Everything.* You said the world doesn't need a savior – but every day I hear people crying out for one. I'm sorry I left you, Lois. I'll take you back now."

He took Lois back to the roof of the Daily Planet building. When she went inside, Superman left for the Fortress of Solitude.

"Father, it's been a long time since I've come to you, but I've never felt so alone." Superman said. He was met with silence. "Father?" he called as he realized something was wrong. The Kryptonian crystals were missing!

83

SPECIAL SKILL

Superman's big-screen adventures are fun to watch, but his comic book adventures began all the way back in 1938!

Countless artists have drawn Superman in the comics over the years. Grab a pencil and learn how it's done.

Use your pencil to draw Superman into the second grid by coping the first grid square by square. It has already been started for you, all you need to do is to finish it and colour him in!

You can use this drawing trick on any of the *Superman Returns* characters.

Take an image of your chosen character and divide it into squares.

Then copy the same amount of squares onto some plain paper.

Fill in the squares you have just created by copying from the squares on your picture.

By changing the size of the squares, you can make your copy as big as you want!

WORD UP...

UNSCRAMBLE THESE JUMBLED-UP NAMES TO MATCH THE FACES. ANSWERS ARE BELOW.

1. HOT RELLUX

_____

3. NEISY MOMJL

_____

3. NEAL SILO

_____

4. TALCK KERN

_____

5. THEIR PEWRY

_____

ULTIMATE SUPERMAN

MULTIPLE CHOICE

49. How many years was Superman gone?

a) 3
b) 4
c) 5

50. To what movie (which featured 1950's Superman George Reeves) does Kitty compare waiting for the crystal to work on the train set?

a) *Gone with the Wind*
b) *Psycho*
c) *Rebel Without a Cause*

51. Which of these *Superman Returns* actors has NOT appeared in another movie directed by Bryan Singer?

a) Kevin Spacey (Lex Luthor)
b) James Marsden (Richard White)
c) Kate Bosworth (Lois Lane)

52. What sport was being played in the stadium where Superman set down the airplane?

a) Football
b) Rugby
c) Baseball

53. Where was *Superman Returns* primarily filmed?

a) London, England
b) Sydney, Australia
c) Vancouver, British Columbia, Canada

54. What color is Kal-El's spacesuit, worn on his flight to explore Krypton?

a) Blue/Red
b) Black
c) Silver

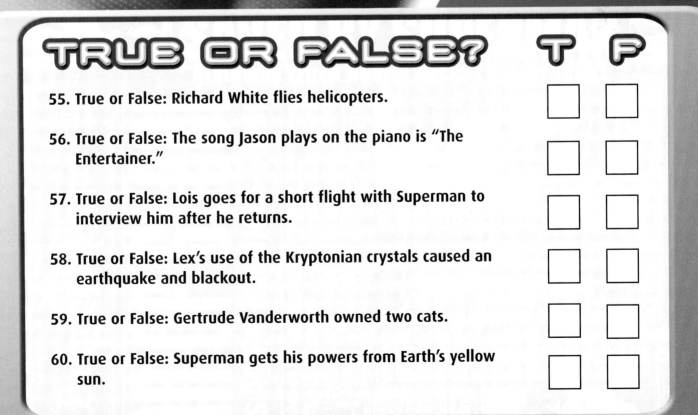

TRUE OR FALSE? T F

55. True or False: Richard White flies helicopters.

56. True or False: The song Jason plays on the piano is "The Entertainer."

57. True or False: Lois goes for a short flight with Superman to interview him after he returns.

58. True or False: Lex's use of the Kryptonian crystals caused an earthquake and blackout.

59. True or False: Gertrude Vanderworth owned two cats.

60. True or False: Superman gets his powers from Earth's yellow sun.

During her research on the blackout, Lois had discovered that the power outage originated at the Vanderworth mansion. Lois and her son, Jason, were on their way to the award ceremony where she was to receive her Pulitzer Prize when she decided to take a small detour to investigate.

She and Jason approached the mansion, but no one answered her knock. Then she heard music coming from the yacht docked behind the mansion. As she and Jason searched for someone aboard the ship, she noticed a display of wigs – Lex Luthor's wigs, she realized with horror.

"This was a bad idea. We have to get out of here," she whispered. Then the yacht's motor roared into life, and the craft pulled away from the dock. Lois grabbed Jason and ran for the door. When she opened it, she was face to face with Lex Luthor.

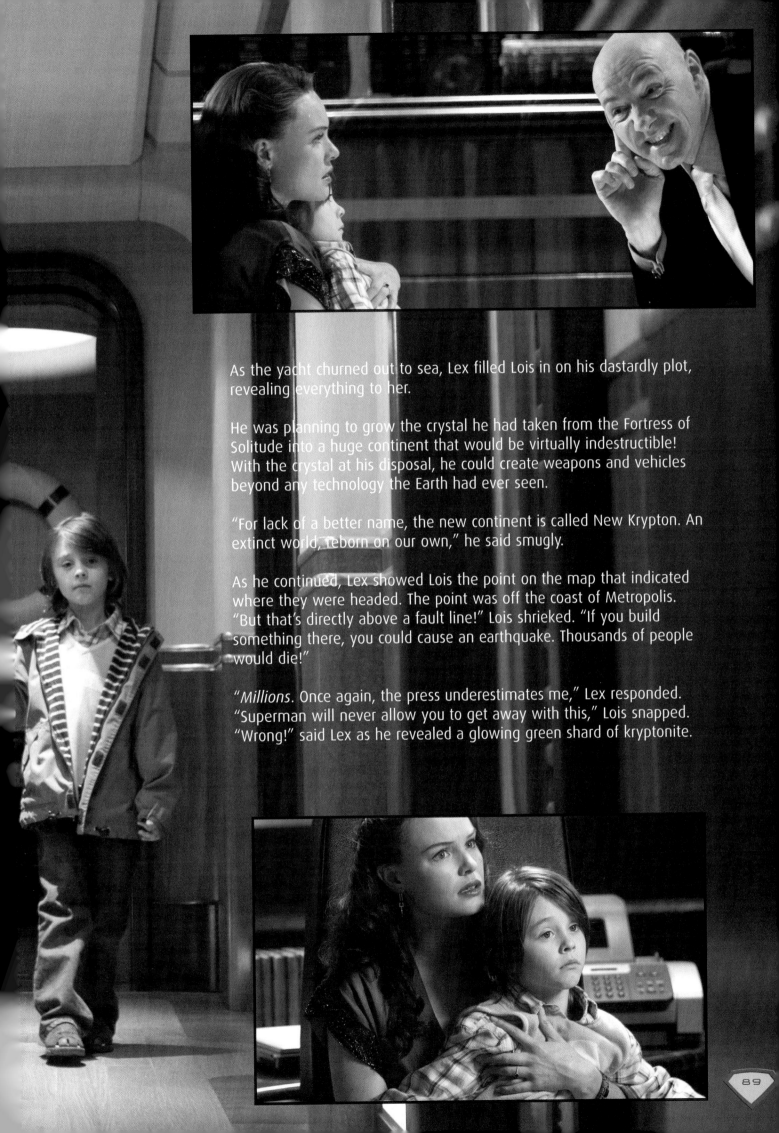

As the yacht churned out to sea, Lex filled Lois in on his dastardly plot, revealing everything to her.

He was planning to grow the crystal he had taken from the Fortress of Solitude into a huge continent that would be virtually indestructible! With the crystal at his disposal, he could create weapons and vehicles beyond any technology the Earth had ever seen.

"For lack of a better name, the new continent is called New Krypton. An extinct world, reborn on our own," he said smugly.

As he continued, Lex showed Lois the point on the map that indicated where they were headed. The point was off the coast of Metropolis. "But that's directly above a fault line!" Lois shrieked. "If you build something there, you could cause an earthquake. Thousands of people would die!"

"*Millions*. Once again, the press underestimates me," Lex responded. "Superman will never allow you to get away with this," Lois snapped. "Wrong!" said Lex as he revealed a glowing green shard of kryptonite.

The ship arrived at the coordinates on Lex's map. Lex took the kryptonite and a white crystal from Superman's fortress and placed them together in the stolen rocket. He left Lois and Jason in the room with his thug Brutus. Up on deck Lex finished securing the crystals in the rocket's compartment and inserted the rocket into the launcher. "Ready, boss?" Stanford asked. With a nod from Lex, the rocket was off. Zoom! The rocket sailed though the sky and arced downward, slamming into the water. As it disappeared into the depths, an eerie glow followed it down. As the rocket hit the ocean floor, it caused another blackout, rippling from the ship to Metropolis. Inside the rocket the crystal started to grow, branching out, melding with the kryptonite. The crystal structure grew so large that it shattered the rocket. The crystal structure continued to grow, digging deep into a chasm in the ocean floor while punching upward to burst through the water's surface and explode into the sky.

Lois, meanwhile, had managed to send a fax that detailed the yacht's coordinates to the Daily Planet bullpen before Brutus unplugged the fax machine. After a struggle, Lois and Jason were locked in the pantry aboard the yacht so they wouldn't cause any more trouble.

At the Daily Planet, Jimmy, Richard, and Clark stared at the fax and realized that it contained sea coordinates, and sprang into action. Richard told Jimmy to call the Coast Guard and to tell Perry that he would take his seaplane. He asked Clark to join him. "No thanks, I get airsick," Clark said, before running to the elevator bank. Whoosh! Through the elevator shaft, Superman tore out of the Daily Planet building and to the coordinates Lois had faxed. As he soared out of the city and over the water, he realized something much worse was happening – using his X-ray vision, he peered into the water and saw the ocean floor splitting open. The crack was travelling fast, right towards Metropolis! If he didn't stop it, the entire city would be destroyed!

Perry was asking Jimmy about the fax when they heard the rumbling. It seemed faint at first, but then hundreds of car alarms went off and the building began to tremble.

Outside, debris rained down all over the city as the split in the ocean floor neared land. Huge cracks ripped through the city streets. Manhole covers and cars exploded everywhere.

As Superman zoomed into the city, two skyscrapers began to crumble from the strain. Thinking fast, he lifted a huge crane and propped it between the two buildings, keeping them from crashing down onto the hysterical crowd below.

Perry White and his staff stood outside the Daily Planet building while chaos reigned all around them. The giant Daily Planet globe that sat atop the building came loose and began to fall. Just as it was about to slam into the street, Superman caught it and placed it gently on the ground.

Lex and his crew were clambering aboard their helicopter when a tidal wave slammed into the yacht, engulfing it in water.

As the yacht listed in the ocean, water spilled through cracks into the pantry, where Lois and Jason were locked in. The water rose higher and higher, until it reached Lois' neck. "Help!" Lois screamed. Just then the door ripped open. Richard had found them with his seaplane!

As they hugged, a huge crystal column shot out of the ocean and pierced the ship's hull, turning the craft upside down as the crystal grew larger. As the ship was raised out of the water, it split in half, sending the broken ship tumbling back into the ocean. The pantry door flew open again for a moment. As Lois raced to catch it, she was knocked unconscious. Water spewed into the tiny room, filling it almost to the ceiling. Just as they were about to give up hope, Superman burst in and carried them to safety.

They stared in awe – all around them were enormous crystal columns that seemed to have grown out of nowhere!
"Take them out of here – and don't come back," Superman said to Richard as they climbed safely into the seaplane.

RETURN OF A HERO

GUESS WHO?

THINK YOU KNOW THE *SUPERMAN RETURNS* CHARACTERS? CHECK OUT THESE PICTURES, AND WRITE YOUR GUESS IN THE SPACE PROVIDED UNDER EACH. THE ANSWERS ARE AT THE BOTTOM OF THE PAGE.

Answers: A -
Superman, B -
Jimmy, C - Louis
Lane, D - Jason,
E - Perry

ULTIMATE SUPERMAN

WRITE THE WORD THAT CORRECTLY COMPLETES THE SENTENCE.

Superman

Bo

Seaplane

Helicopter

Car

Jimmy Olsen

FILL IN THE BLANK

61. _____ is Clark Kent's best friend.

62. Superman saved Kitty when her _____ was about to crash.

63. Richard flies a _____ to save Lois and Jason.

64. _____ is the bartender at Jimmy's favorite pub.

65. Lex flies a _____ to escape from New Krypton.

66. _____ calls flying the safest way to travel.

RETURNS QUIZ PART 6

MATCHING

DRAW A LINE FROM THE CLUE TO THE ANSWER

67. Joe Shuster

68. Brutus

69. Gertrude Vanderworth

70. Richard White

71. Jason

72. Martha Kent

A. Lex's henchman

B. Superman's co-creator

C. *Daily Planet* International section editor

D. Gave Lex her fortune

E. Lives in Smallville

F. Lois's son

NOW THAT YOU HAVE COMPLETED THE ULTIMATE SUPERMAN RETURNS QUIZ, GO TO PAGE 108 TO CHECK YOUR ANSWERS.

Superman flew to the heart of the crystal formation when suddenly it dawned on him – it looked just like Krypton! He swooped down toward the centre of the structures and saw the familiar circle of monoliths, exactly like the ones he had seen on what was left of Krypton. In the centre of the monoliths was a structure that looked almost identical to the Fortress of Solitude. Resting next to it was Lex's helicopter.

However, unlike Krypton, Superman felt life all around him here.
"See anything familiar?" Lex Luthor asked, sneering.

"I don't have time for this. You have something that belongs to me, Luthor," Superman said, storming toward Lex to get his crystal back.

BAM! Lex punched Superman in the face, knocking him to the ground. In shock, Superman realized that his nose was bleeding!

Onboard the seaplane Lois had regained consciousness.
"It's all right, we're safe," Richard said.
Remembering the kryptonite, Lois screamed. "Richard, we have to turn around!" Nodding in agreement, Richard flew back toward the crystals.

Meanwhile, Lex continued his assault on Superman.
"I didn't send you to die on Krypton just to have you come back and stop me now!"
All at once Superman realized that he had been tricked! "You...why?"
"You robbed me of five years of my life," Lex spat. "I just returned the favor."
As Superman thought about the years of his life he had wasted in hopes of finding Krypton, he realized he was getting sicker and sicker.

"Didn't your mother ever tell you to look before you leap?" Lex taunted.
Superman used his fading X-ray vision and discovered that the entire crystal structure was filled with kryptonite. It was draining all the energy from his body!
"Kryptonite. Amazing, isn't it?" Lex laughed as Superman writhed in pain.

"Fly! Come on, fly!" Luthor shouted as he kicked Superman.

Lex's henchmen surrounded Superman. As they pummelled him, Superman drained the last of his strength using X-ray vision to locate his father's crystal. It was deep inside a crevice, surrounded by kryptonite. Soon after, his X-ray vision faded. His power was gone.

"There's no place for you anymore, Superman."
As Lex continued his assault, Superman gathered his last remaining strength and dragged himself toward the ledge of the crystal structure. He found himself at the edge of a steep cliff that dropped off straight into the ocean.

Superman screamed in pain as Lex stabbed him in the back with a shard of kryptonite. He looked over the ledge, then fell into the water.
"So long, Superman," Lex Luthor said, with an evil laugh.

Superman plunged deep into the water and tumbled downward. He struggled to pull out the shard of kryptonite that was embedded in his back, but he couldn't reach it.

As around him crystals were growing in every direction. The faint glow of green from the growing kryptonite illuminated the water around him. Superman struggled to swim to the surface, but he was too weak to move. A mesh of crystals quickly began to encase him!

Above the water Richard circled in the seaplane around the area where Superman had fallen into the ocean. Lois threw open the door of the seaplane and jumped into the raging waters as soon as the plane touched down!

As Lois reached Superman, one last bubble of air escaped from his mouth. Lois grabbed onto Superman's cape and dragged him away from the crystals. She gasped for air as she surfaced with Superman in her arms.

"Wake up! Come on, wake up!" Lois screamed. Superman came to and gasped, "Kryptonite. There's kryptonite in the crystals."

Lois and Richard knew they had to get Superman away from the crystals if there was any chance of saving him, but the water was too choppy for the plane to take off.

Around them crystal pillars rose fast. The plane barely made it through two giant formations that shot out of the water.

"Seatbelts!" Richard shouted as he manoeuvred through the growing crystal columns.

Just when they thought they were safe, several crystal columns grew beneath them. The plane was now thousands of feet above the ocean – and heading toward a waterfall! They almost tumbled over the waterfall, but the plane managed to catch a strong air current and remained airborne.

Then Lois noticed the shard of kryptonite in Superman's back. She pulled it out and threw it from the plane.

Superman slowly began to regain strength. Out of the window he saw New Krypton – still growing. Soon it would take over everything!

"I have to go back," Superman said firmly. "Goodbye, Lois." He flew out of the plane and toward New Krypton. As he flew, the warm yellow light of the Earth's sun helped him regain the superstrength the kryptonite had drained from his body. When he was strong enough again, he dove straight into the ocean.

Superman used his heat vision to melt the Earth's crust as he disappeared under the ocean floor.

Lex, Kitty, and the crew felt the crystal structure start to rumble all around them. They looked up to see the horizon moving – they were rising into the air!
"NO!" Lex screamed as huge crystal structures began to shatter all around him. "Get to the helicopter. Now!"

Lex and Kitty piled into the helicopter, and Lex, panic-stricken, started the engines. The helicopter roared to life, but too late – the ground beneath it crumbled away. It plummeted into the foaming chasm below. Soon, however, Lex gained control of the helicopter and escaped, looking on in horror as New Krypton lifted higher into the sky.

Huge waves rippled outward as the enormous mass of crystals rose out of the ocean. When its base broke the surface, it was encased in a mass of brown, rocky earth – and below it was Superman!

Higher and higher Superman flew with New Krypton overhead as giant chunks of crystals fell off, exposing kryptonite.
In agony Superman drew on the last ounce of his strength as he entered space with the giant crystal formation. With a final burst of power, Superman hurled the structure off into deep space. Unconscious, Superman descended to Earth. Faster and faster he fell, until the air around him blazed bright orange as he re-entered Earth's atmosphere.
An orange streak shot across the sky high above Metropolis, hurling closer and closer, until WHAM! Superman landed in a park, sending debris flying hundreds of feet into the air.

As the dust cleared, there was a monstrous crater. Superman had landed.

Superman was still unconscious when he was finally removed from the crater his impact had created. He was rushed to the hospital where he remained unconscious for some time.

Lois Lane visited Superman in the hospital. She realized she had been wrong about the world not needing him – now, more than ever, the world needed Superman.

When he finally recovered, Superman let Lois knew that he was all right. He also told her that he would never leave her again. He knew now that Earth was – and always would be – his home.

Lex Luthor has learned how to grow a new continent by using Kryptonian crystals and water.

You can grow your own Kryptonian crystals by following the steps below.

Make sure to get permission from an adult before making them, and get help in using the hot water!

WHAT YOU NEED

- Hot water (near boiling)

- A thin piece of thread

- Sugar

- A Bowl

- A jar

- A pencil

KRYPTONIAN CRYSTALS

WHAT TO DO

Step 1: Ask an adult to pour hot water (almost boiling) into a bowl.

Step 2: Slowly add sugar until it all has all dissolved in the hot water, and no more can be dissolved.

Step 3: Pour water/sugar mixture into a jar.

(**Optional Step:** Add Green Food Coloring to the mixture to create kryptonite!)

Step 4: Tie a piece of string or thread to the middle of the pencil.

Step 5: Lower the string into the jar, resting the pencil on the top of the jar, holding the string in the center of the jar.

Step 6: Wait for 15 minutes, and swish the jar around, careful not to spill it. Wait 15 more minutes, and spin the jar again. Then wait one hour, and swish it for the final time.

Step 7: Place the jar in a warm place where it will not be disturbed. Crystals should start to grow, and will get bigger over the next week. At the end of a week (or so), pull the string out of the jar by the pencil. You should have new crystals!

Just don't use them to grow a new continent!

ANSWERS

70-72 - YOU ARE SUPERMAN!

60-69 - THAT'S A LOT OF
KNOWLEDGE!
ARE YOU REALLY
CLARK KENT?

50-59 - LOIS WON A
PULITZER
PRIZE FOR
KNOWING THAT
MUCH!

40-49 - WITH INFORMATION
LIKE THAT, YOU COULD
DEFEAT LEX LUTHOR.

30-39 - JIMMY OLSEN WILL HELP YOU
WITH MORE RESEARCH.

20-29 - MAYBE YOU WERE GONE FOR
FIVE YEARS, AND NEED TO
CATCH UP.

10-19 - WERE YOU IN PRISON WITH
LEX'S FRIENDS?

0-9 - THERE MUST BE SOME
KRYPTONITE NEARBY.

YOUR SCORE:

PAGE 1: 1.False, 2. False, 3. True, 14. False, 5. False, 6. True. **PAGE 2**: a) Jason, b) Two life sentences., b) Krypton, a) Lois Lane in *The Adventures of Superman*, b) The *Daily Planet*, c) Shelby. **PAGE 3:** b) Martha, a) Kal, c) Gertrude, c) Ace o' Clubs, b) *Explorer*, b) Smallville. **PAGE 4:** Answers: 19/D; 20/A; 21/F; 22/C; 23/B; 24/E. **PAGE 5:** b) The Arctic, a) *Action Comics* #1, "Why the World Doesn't Need Superman", c) Ian, b) *Smallville* (as Jimmy Olsen's father), c) Aquaman. **PAGE 6:** 31. True, 32. True, 33. False, 34. True, 35. False, 36. True. **PAGE 7:** 37. Jason, 38. Cameraphone, 39. Heat vision, 40. Lex Luthor, 41. Kryptonite, 42. Coordinates. **PAGE 8:** Answers: 43/C; 44/E; 45/F; 46/D; 47/B; 48/A. **PAGE 9:** c) 5, a) *Gone with the Wind*, c) Kate Bosworth (Lois Lane), c) Baseball, b) Sydney, Australia, c) Silver. PAGE 10- 55. False, 56. True, 57. True, 58. True, 59. False, 60. True. **PAGE 11:** 61) Jimmy, 62) Car, 63) Seaplane, 64) Bo, 65) Helicopter, 66) Superman. **PAGE 12:** Answers: 67/B; 68/A; 69/D; 70/C; 71/F; 72/E

CLARK KENT TO SUPERMAN

Clark Kent needs to find somewhere to change into Superman! Help him find an empty room in the *Daily Planet*, where he can change. Find your way through the maze of corridors but don't get confused and end up outside with Jimmy or in Perry's office!